TRINIT
GUILDI

Aural Book 2

Specimen Aural Tests
for Trinity Guildhall examinations
from 2007

Grades 6-8

BEWARE!

DISC C528

Published by:
Trinity College London
89 Albert Embankment
London SE1 7TP UK

T +44 (0)20 7820 6100
F +44 (0)20 7820 6161
E music@trinityguildhall.co.uk
www.trinityguildhall.co.uk

Editor: Natasha Witts
Music processed by New Notations London
Printed in England by Halstan & Co. Ltd, Amersha

D0785744

Acknowledgements

Trinity Guildhall gratefully acknowledges the contribution of Tim Grant-Jones, the author of the book and pianist on the CD.

In addition, thanks are extended to Paul Ayres, Keith Beniston, David Gaukroger, Rosemary Harris, Derek Hyde, Robin Jackson, Ben Norbury, Prof. Ken Pickering, Roger Pope, Mark Stringer, Claire Webb and Naomi Yandell, as well as all the teachers, students and examiners around the world whose advice has contributed to the development of this suite of tests.

Introduction

Aural skill – the ability to listen intelligently to music and to understand what has been heard - forms a vital part of the training of musicians at all levels. The assessment of this skill in practical examinations ensures that it is developed alongside instrumental (or vocal) ability.

A new suite of aural tests has been developed for use in Trinity Guildhall examinations from 2007. By answering a series of questions all based on the same piece of music, candidates will find that they develop their ability to listen with perception. This process is enhanced by sections of the tests which encourage reading skills and eye-to-ear co-ordination. As far as possible these tests require instinctive responses, and depend much less than previously on the singing of melodies and on in-depth theoretical knowledge. In many cases candidates should find that the kind of responses needed arise quite naturally out of the continuing development of their practical musical skills, and will in turn assist in widening the growing musician's experience and enjoyment.

Using this book:

This **Aural Book** is designed to be used effectively either by teachers during lessons or by candidates themselves at home. As teachers will generally wish to supply their own explanations of the questions, the text is addressed primarily to the candidate.

For each grade the following information is given:

About the test piece – gives the parameters of the test piece, so that candidates understand the features of the piece, and so that teachers may devise further sample tests if they wish.

What the examiner will do – explains exactly how the examiner will run the test, so that candidates can feel at ease in the examination and so that teachers can run the tests in the same way.

What you will be asked to do – explains exactly what the candidate will be asked to do for each question, so that candidates and teachers clearly understand what the task involves.

What the question is for – explains the musical reasons for the question, enabling candidates and teachers to understand the skills being developed and assessed.

Hints for candidates – gives useful tips on how to prepare and succeed at each test, and covers both valuable musical knowledge and practical hints for the examination itself.

Information for teachers – gives an overview of the rationale for each section of the tests, highlights the progression of each skill through the grades and gives tips for adapting the tests to ask a wider selection of questions.

At the end of each grade candidates are invited to try the sample tests, either by using the CD or with their teacher playing the questions on the piano.

The **Answer Booklet** contains the text and printed music from the CD so that teachers may play the examples for their pupils.

Each example is also annotated with the answers clearly indicated, so that candidates may be assisted in their preparation by parents or friends with limited (or no) musical knowledge.

The examples use a variety of styles and are suitable for a range of pianistic abilities. They are not exhaustive, but give ample practice material, while the parameters of the test piece are given at each grade to enable teachers to select suitable supplementary material if necessary.

Using the CD:

Each track contains a complete set of questions including spoken text and music. The text and music from the CD may be found in the **Answer Booklet** along with answers to the questions.

Tips for preparing for the aural tests

- The questions for Grades 6–8 cover many aspects of music, including:
    - metre
    - phrasing
    - style
    - dynamics
    - articulation
    - rhythm
    - texture
    - tonality
- You can practise most of the aural tests with most types of music, including pieces you play or sing and those you listen to, so you can start to prepare for your exam well in advance.
- Find out the title of each piece of music you listen to or play. As well, you should look for the name of the composer, artist or band who created it, as well as seeing when it was written. Knowing the date will help you identify the different styles of music, for example Baroque in the 17th and 18th centuries, Romantic in the 19th century, or jazz and rock in the 20th and 21st.
- Try to listen to music in an active way. Don't just hear the sound that the music makes, but ask yourself questions about what is going on. It can be useful to concentrate on just one aspect at a time. Here are some other questions you could ask about the music you listen to:
    - Are there any elements of the music's style that you have heard before?
    - Is the composer or artist one that you know? How is this piece like other works of theirs?
    - Is the texture thick or thin?
    - What feeling (if any) does the music express?
    - What instruments are playing – are they acoustic or electronic?
    - Does the harmony do what you would expect or is it full of surprises?
    - Can you hear recognisable chords? Are there cadences?
- As you can see, there are many, many questions you can ask about any piece of music you hear. You will not spot everything in one hearing, and there is no reason why you should! Music can take a very long time to create, and this can be because the composer is putting so much into the piece. It is no surprise, therefore, that it can take listeners a long time to work their way through all the different layers; but this is what makes music so fascinating and satisfying for so many millions of people all around the world.

Grade 6

About the test piece:

metre $\frac{2}{4}, \frac{3}{4}, \frac{4}{4}$ or $\frac{6}{8}$

key major

style piano style using treble and bass clef

features contains a modulation to the dominant, subdominant or relative minor

All questions will be based on the same piece of music.

Question 1

What the examiner will do:
Play a short piece in a major key in $\frac{2}{4}, \frac{3}{4}, \frac{4}{4}$ or $\frac{6}{8}$ twice.

What you will be asked to do:
Tell the examiner the time signature. Comment on the main features of the piece such as phrasing, style and dynamics. You will have the opportunity to give comments after the first and/or second playing.

What the question is for:
- To learn to recognise the **time signature** of a piece;
- To develop your skills in recognising **how the music is being played**;
- To learn the **words** to describe what you hear.

Hints
- **Conducting** (or clapping or tapping) as you listen is the easiest and most effective way to work out the time signature. Don't forget that the time might be **simple** (beat easily divisible by 2) or **compound** (beat easily divisible by 3). See **Aural Book 1** for more information on conducting.
- **Phrasing** acts as punctuation in the music and shows where the 'breaths' are. Phrases often occur in two- or four-bar lengths. If the phrases are the same length throughout, the phrasing is **regular**; if the phrases are of different lengths the phrasing is **irregular**. Remember that phrases can begin and end part way through a bar.
- The main features of the music all go to make up the **style**. To determine this, listen to features such as the shape of the melody, the harmony, how the dynamics and other expressive detail are used, how the different sections of the music relate to each other, and so on. All these give clues to the style of the music.
- The **dynamic** changes add interest to the piece. Listen first for the overall dynamic plan from phrase to phrase. Then listen for rising and falling within phrases, echo effects and feminine endings (phrase endings finishing on a weaker sound on a weaker beat, as in the word 'music').

Question 2

What the examiner will do:

Play the final section of the piece once.

What you will be asked to do:

Tell the examiner what cadence comes at the end (perfect, imperfect, plagal or interrupted).

What the question is for:

- To develop your skills in recognising **chord progressions and phrase endings**;
- To learn the **words** to describe what you hear.

> **Hints**
> - Make sure you know what these four cadences sound like in a major key.
> - The **perfect cadence** is the only cadence at this grade that feels like a strong ending (full stop). It consists of a dominant chord (V) followed by a tonic chord (I).
> - The **plagal cadence** also feels like an ending, but is slightly weaker. It consists of a subdominant chord (IV) followed by a tonic chord (I). It is often used in church services to sing the word 'Amen'.
> - The **imperfect cadence** feels open ended and unfinished, like a comma, or as if asking a question that needs an answering phrase. It consists of one of several chords followed by a dominant chord (V).
> - The **interrupted cadence** feels as if it is going to finish but has a surprise final chord. It consists of a dominant chord (V) followed by a submediant chord (vi). An interrupted cadence in a major key will finish on a minor chord.
> - The chord names are given for information: you only need to learn the names of the cadences, so concentrate on how they sound.

Question 3

What the examiner will do:

Play the key chord of the opening key of the piece and state the key. Then play once a section of the piece which modulates.

What you will be asked to do:

Tell the examiner into which key the music has modulated: the dominant, subdominant or relative minor. The answer may be given as either the key or the technical name (e.g. in C major: 'to G' or 'to the dominant').

What the question is for:

- To develop your skills in recognising **key changes (modulations)**;
- To learn the **words** to describe what you hear.

Hints

- You need to know each **major key** up to three sharps or flats and its **dominant, subdominant and relative minor**.
- Learn the **circle of 5ths** for major keys. By now, you should have played (or sung) music and scales/arpeggios in most of these keys.
- Remember, you can state the key or the technical name in your answer.
- If you want to state the actual modulated key, think of the possible modulated keys as soon as you are told the key of the piece, e.g. C major could go to G (the dominant), to F (the subdominant) or to A minor (the relative minor).
- A modulation to the **dominant** feels as if something bright and exciting has happened. A modulation to the **subdominant** can feel less important.
- The music is in a major key, so if it modulates to a minor key, it will be to the **relative minor**.
- Try holding the tonic note in your head or singing it quietly; if the modulation is to the subdominant or the relative minor the original tonic note will still fit with the tonic chord of the new key. If the original tonic note clashes with the new tonic chord then the piece has modulated to the dominant.

The circle of 5ths

The dominant key is the next key to the tonic following the circle clockwise (adding a sharp to, or removing a flat from, the key signature).
The subdominant key is the next key to the tonic following the circle anticlockwise (removing a sharp from, or adding a flat to, the key signature).
The relative minor is the minor key that shares the key signature of the tonic.
The diagram shows the tonic, dominant and subdominant keys in C major.

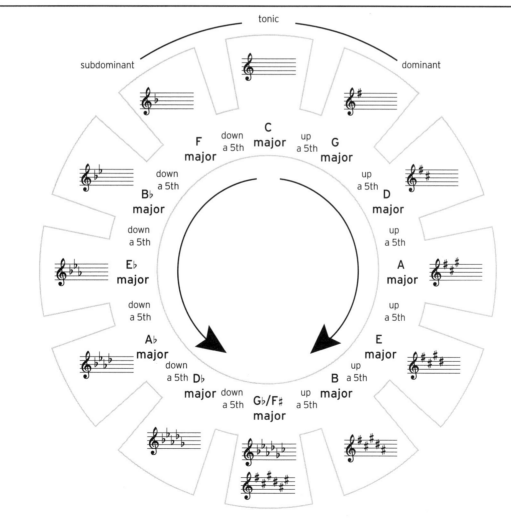

Question 4

What the examiner will do:
Give you a printed copy of the piece. Play the piece twice in a version with two changes to the top (melody) line. These may be to the rhythm, pitch or articulation.

What you will be asked to do:
Identify where the changes took place and what they were.

What the question is for:
- To develop your **musical memory**;
- To develop your **awareness of rhythm, pitch and articulation**;
- To develop your skills in **relating the music you see to what you hear**;
- To improve the **accuracy of your reading**.

Hints
- You will already have heard the complete original version **twice** before hearing the changed version, as well as two sections of the piece.
- Try to concentrate on **listening** to the melody while you are following the printed music.
- Remember that you are not allowed to make any marks on the copy of the music you have been given. You could point your finger at the first change to help you remember where it was while you look and listen for the second change.
- Use the printed copy to tell the examiner where the changes occurred and identify each as a rhythm, pitch or articulation change.
- For a pitch change, you should explain what note was played instead of the printed one.
- For a rhythm change, you should explain how the rhythm was different.
- If the articulation changed you should explain whether it changed from staccato to legato or vice versa and identify exactly which notes were altered.
- Be as accurate as possible in your answers. A basic answer will state where the changes were and what kind of change was made. If you can tell the examiner exactly which notes were changed and what they changed to, this will result in a higher mark.

Try the tests

01 - 10   Listen to the CD or ask your teacher to play the tests for you. Each track on the CD contains a complete set of questions. Printed on pages 7-11 is the music you will need for Question 4 of each set. Don't look at the music until you reach Question 4. The answers to the tests can be found in the **Answer Booklet**, pages 2-11.

Music for Grade 6 Question 4

01 Test 1

02 Test 2

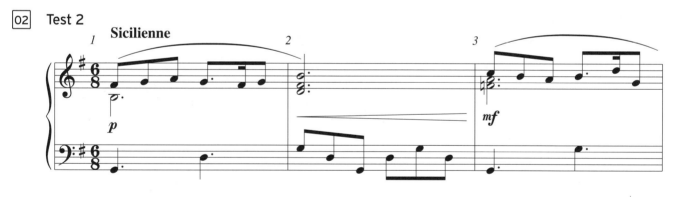

03 **Test 3**

04 **Test 4**

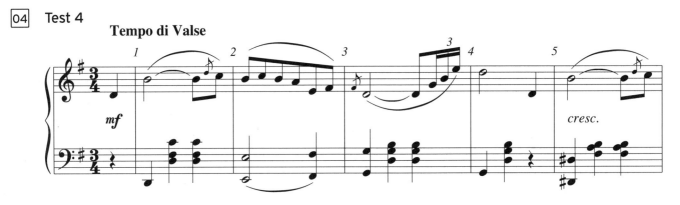

05 **Test 5**

06 **Test 6**

07 Test 7

08 Test 8

09 Test 9

Tempo di Minuet

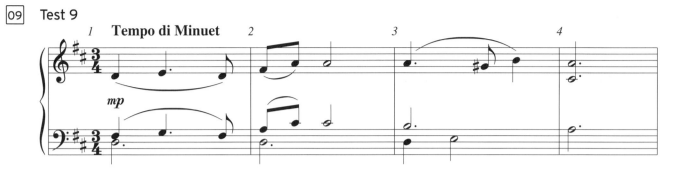

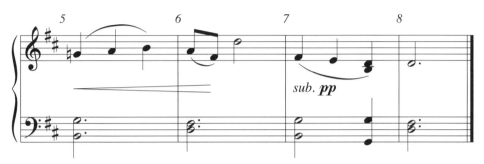

10 Test 10

Tempo di Rumba

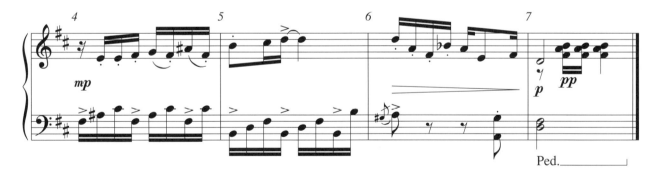

Grade 7

About the test piece:

metre	any commonly used time signature
key	minor
style	piano style using treble and bass clef
features	contains at least one cadence

All questions will be based on the same piece of music.

Question 1

What the examiner will do:

Play a short piece in a minor key twice.

What you will be asked to do:

Comment on the main features of the piece such as style, phrasing and dynamics. You will have the opportunity to give comments after the first and/or second playing.

What the question is for:

- To develop your skills in recognising **how the music is being played**;
- To learn the **words** to describe what you hear.

Hints

- The style of the music is like the type of food a restaurant serves; there can be many different dishes but they may all be the same style: Italian, Greek, Chinese etc. The main features of the music all go to make up the **style**. To determine this, listen to features such as the shape of the melody, harmony, how the dynamics and other expressive detail are used, how the different sections of the music relate to each other, and so on. All these give clues to the style of the music.
- Certain characteristics might also lead you to suggest a particular period of music in which it might have been written. Listening to and playing a wide range of pieces is the best way to learn to identify different musical styles.
- **Phrasing** acts as punctuation in the music and shows where the 'breaths' are. Phrases often occur in two- or four-bar lengths. If the phrases are the same length throughout, the phrasing is **regular**; if the phrases are of different lengths the phrasing is **irregular**. Remember that phrases can begin and end part way through a bar.
- The **dynamic** changes add interest to the piece. Listen first for the overall dynamic plan from phrase to phrase. Then listen for rising and falling within phrases, echo effects and feminine endings (phrase endings finishing on a weaker sound on a weaker beat, as in the word 'music').
- Listen for **compositional devices** such as sequences, pedal notes, chromatic passages and/or notes, dotted rhythms, cadences, passing notes, repetition, imitation, syncopation and anacruses, and refer to these in your answer.

Question 2

What the examiner will do:
Play a section of the piece once.

What you will be asked to do:
Identify its cadence (perfect, imperfect, plagal or interrupted).

What the question is for:
- To develop your skills in recognising **chord progressions and phrase endings**;
- To learn the **words** to describe what you hear.

> Hints
> - Make sure you know what these four cadences sound like in a minor key.
> - The **perfect cadence** is the only cadence at this grade that feels like a strong ending (full stop). In a minor key it consists of a dominant chord (V) followed by a tonic chord (i).
> - The **plagal cadence** also feels like an ending, but is slightly weaker. In a minor key it consists of a subdominant chord (iv) followed by a tonic chord (i). It is often used in church services to sing the word 'Amen'.
> - The **imperfect cadence** feels open ended and unfinished, like a comma, or as if asking a question that needs an answering phrase. It consists of one of several chords followed by a dominant chord (V).
> - The **interrupted cadence** feels as if it is going to finish but has a surprise final chord. It consists of a dominant chord (V) followed by a submediant chord (VI). An interrupted cadence in a minor key will finish on a major chord.
> - The chord names are given for information: you only need to learn the names of the cadences, so concentrate on how they sound.

Question 3

What the examiner will do:
Give you a printed copy of the first section of the piece and then play twice a version with three changes. These may be to the pitch (of the top (melody) line only) or to the rhythm.

What you will be asked to do:
Identify where the changes took place and what type of changes they were.

What the question is for:
- To develop **memory skills**;
- To develop awareness of **changes of rhythm and pitch**;
- To develop skills in **relating the music you see to what you hear**;
- To improve the **accuracy of your reading**.

Hints
- Remember there will not be pitch changes to the bass line, but learn to watch both lines carefully for changes in rhythm.
- Remember that you are not allowed to make any marks on the copy of the music you have been given. You could point your finger at the first change to help you remember where it was while you look and listen for the other changes, or say out loud any changes you notice as they happen.
- Use the printed copy to show the examiner where the changes occurred and identify each as a rhythm or pitch change.

Question 4

What the examiner will do:

State the key and play the key chord of the opening key of the piece. Then play the piece once with a changed ending. (Part of the piece may be omitted by the examiner for clarity if appropriate.)

What you will be asked to do:

Tell the examiner into which key the music has modulated: the subdominant minor, the relative major or the dominant of the relative major (e.g. G major in A minor). The answer may be given as either the key or the technical name (e.g. in C minor: 'to E flat' or 'to the relative major').

What the question is for:

- To develop your skills in recognising **key changes (modulation)**;
- To learn the **words** to describe what you hear.

Hints
- You need to know each **minor key** up to three sharps or flats and its **subdominant minor, relative major and dominant of the relative major**.
- Learn the **circle of 5ths** for minor keys. Write the minor keys into the circle of 5ths on page 5 if you need to. By now, you should have played (or sung) music and scales/arpeggios in most of these keys.
- Remember, you can state the key or the technical name in your answer.
- Modulating to a new key is often achieved by playing the **dominant 7th** chord of that key. This leads straight to the new key.
- There are three possible modulations, one to another minor key and the other two to major keys.

- A modulation to the **subdominant minor** (chord iv) is the easiest one to recognise because it is the only one to a minor key at this grade. A common way to get to this key is to play the (minor) tonic chord, turn it from minor to major and add a 7th. It can now function as the dominant 7th of the subdominant. Here is an example in A minor:

original key:	i	I (major)	I⁷	iv
new key:	-	V	V⁷	i
	A minor	A major	A⁷	D minor

- In a modulation to the **relative major** (chord III), the flattened 7th of the original key becomes the root note of the dominant 7th chord in the new key. Here is an example in A minor:

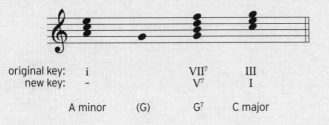

original key:	i		VII⁷	III
new key:	-		V⁷	I
	A minor	(G)	G⁷	C major

- A modulation to the **dominant of the relative major** (chord VII) is not as difficult to understand as you might think. Here, the music modulates a little further away than to the relative major. It is one key further around the circle of 5ths. The (minor) tonic can be thought of as the supertonic in the new key, which leads naturally to the dominant in a classic ii-V⁷-I progression. Here is an example in A minor:

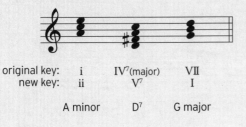

original key:	i	IV⁷(major)	VII
new key:	ii	V⁷	I
	A minor	D⁷	G major

Try the tests

11 - 17   Listen to the CD or ask your teacher to play the tests for you. Each track on the CD contains a complete set of questions. Printed on pages 16 and 17 is the music you need for Question 3 of each set. Don't look at the music until you reach Question 3. The answers to the tests can be found in the **Answer Booklet**, pages 12-23.

Music for Grade 7 Question 3

11 Test 1

12 Test 2

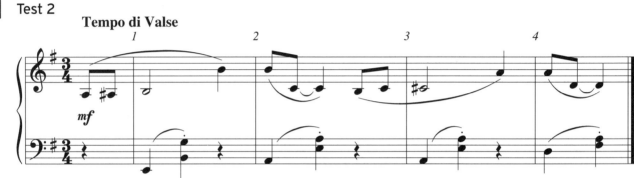

13 Test 3

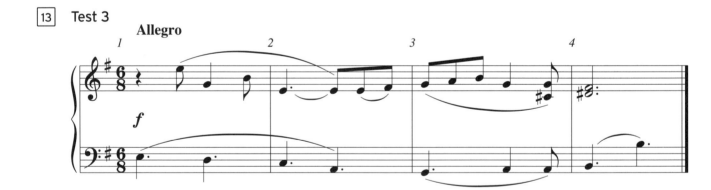

14 Test 4

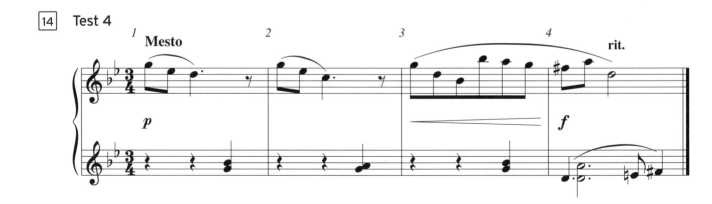

15 Test 5

16 Test 6

17 Test 7

Grade 8

About the test piece:

key   major, minor, bitonal, modal or atonal

style   piano style using treble and bass clef

All questions will be based on the same piece of music.

Question 1

What the examiner will do:

Play a short piece twice.

What you will be asked to do:

Comment on the main features of the pieces such as phrasing, style, dynamics, articulation, rhythm and texture. You will have the opportunity to give comments after the first and/or second playing.

What the question is for:

* To develop your skills in recognising **how the music is being played**;
* To learn the **words** to describe what you hear.

Hints
* There is a lot to remember so you should think about the **vocabulary** you will need to explain what you hear. Remember also that there will be more to say about some of these headings than others. It all depends on the piece.

* **Phrasing** acts as punctuation in the music and shows where the 'breaths' are. Phrases often occur in two- or four-bar lengths. If the phrases are the same length throughout, the phrasing is **regular**; if the phrases are of different lengths the phrasing is **irregular**. Remember that phrases can begin and end part way through a bar.

* The style of the music is like the type of food a restaurant serves; there can be many different dishes but they may all be the same style: Italian, Greek, Chinese etc. The main features of the music all go to make up the **style**. To determine this, listen to features such as the shape of the melody, the harmony, how the dynamics and other expressive details are used, how the different sections of the music relate to each other, and so on. All these give clues to the style of the music.
* Certain characteristics might also lead you to suggest a particular period in which it might have been written. Listening to and playing a wide range of pieces is the best way to learn to identify different musical styles.

- The **dynamic** changes add interest to the piece. Listen first for the overall dynamic plan from phrase to phrase. Then listen for rising and falling within phrases, echo effects and feminine endings (phrase endings finishing on a weaker sound on a weaker beat, as in the word 'music').

- The piece may use a mixture of staccato and legato notes. Explain how the **articulation** is used referring to any distinctive features in the piece.

- You are not expected to describe the **rhythm** of the entire piece, but you should be able to mention:
  - the kind of time (simple or compound)
  - the time signature

  Other characteristics you might notice are:
  - syncopation and use of ties
  - any other significant rhythmic features

- **Texture** describes how the musical lines work together. Make sure you know how to describe textures as:
  - monophonic (a single line, no harmony or accompaniment)
  - homophonic (all sounds moving with the same rhythm)
  - polyphonic (several musical ideas moving independently)

  There are other ways of explaining texture such as:
  - unison or octaves
  - 2-part, 3-part, 4-part
  - imitative

  As the piece will be played on the piano, you might want to describe piano figurations, such as:
  - waltz-style accompaniment ('oom cha cha')
  - march-style accompaniment ('oom pah')
  - tune in bass or middle of texture

  The texture might also be sparse or dense, or concentrated in one or two particular registers.

- Listen for **compositional devices** such as sequences, pedal notes, chromatic passages and/or notes, dotted rhythms, cadences, passing notes, repetition, imitation, syncopation and anacruses, and refer to these in your answer.

- Listen to the **tonality** of the piece and think about whether it:
  - was major, minor, bitonal, modal or atonal
  - modulated and if possible, say where to and how
  - used mainly diatonic or chromatic harmony
  - used particular chords such as dominant 7ths, diminished chords or other coloured harmonies

Question 2

What the examiner will do:

Give you a printed copy of the piece. Play the piece once as originally heard and then play twice a version with three changes. These may be to the rhythm, melody, harmony, articulation, dynamics or tempo, and may occur in the treble or bass clef lines, or both.

What you will be asked to do:

Identify where the changes took place and what type of changes they were.

What the question is for:

* To develop **memory skills**;
* To develop awareness of **changes of rhythm, pitch, harmony, articulation, dynamics and tempo**;
* To develop skills in **relating the music you see to what you hear**;
* To improve the **accuracy of your reading**.

Hints

* So far you have only had to identify pitch changes to the **melody** at the top of the texture and in the treble clef. Remember, for Grade 8 changes might occur in the bass clef or inner parts too.
* Make sure you are used to reading music in the **bass clef** as well as music using **two clefs** (most piano music). If you play an instrument that doesn't use bass clef, try playing some bass clef music up an octave or two.
* Make sure you know the common markings for **dynamics**, **tempo** and **articulation**.
* Remember that you are not allowed to make any marks on the copy of the music you have been given. You could point your finger at the first change to help you remember where it was while you look and listen for the other changes, or say out loud any changes you notice as they happen.

Try the tests

18 - 24   Listen to the CD or ask your teacher to play the tests for you. Each track on the CD contains a complete set of questions. Printed on pages 21-24 is the music you need for Question 2 of each set. Don't look at the music until you reach Question 2. The answers to the tests can be found in the **Answer Booklet**, pages 24-34.

Music for Grade 8 Question 2

18 Test 1

19 Test 2

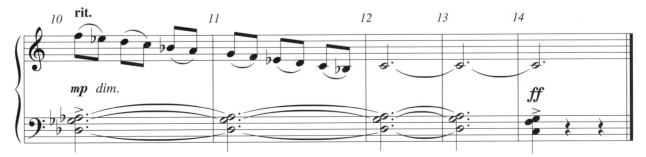

20 Test 3

Melancolico

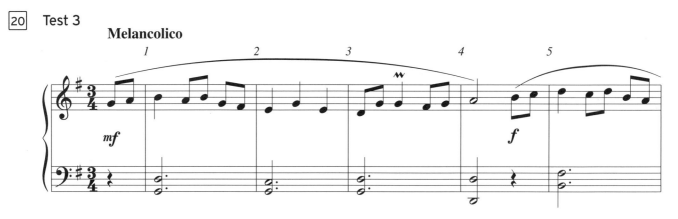

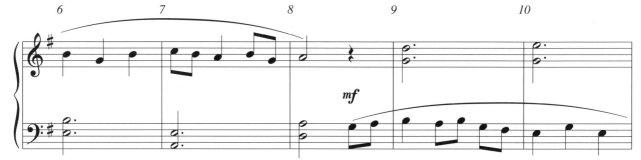

21 Test 4

Con espressione

22 **Test 5**

Cakewalk

23 **Test 6**

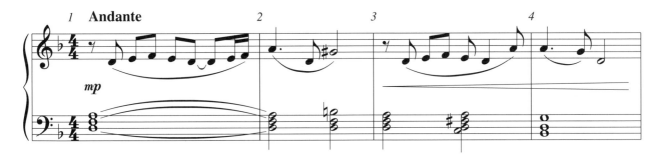

24 **Test 7**

Information for teachers

Instrumentation

In the examination the tests will be played on the piano. In lessons they may be played live or delivered using the CD. Teachers should note that most tests need to be played on the piano owing to the integral nature of the harmony and texture at these grades.

Significant features of the test piece

The first question asked at each grade is concerned with exploring candidates' perception of the characteristics of the piece and the performance. As they proceed through the grades, candidates will find that the areas they are asked about become less specific, allowing them to bring their perceptual skills into play and to develop their own approach to listening and understanding.

The general heading of style allows candidates to comment on any noteworthy aspects of metre, rhythm, texture, dynamics, phrasing, articulation and tonality, as well as any particular compositional devices used, and to bring these together into an explanation of what gives a particular piece its individual 'feel'. Candidates who are able to use their observations to put the test piece into a stylistic context will be approaching the essence of this question; the styles of music are widely varied, and listening and discussion based on a wide range of pieces will provide good preparation for this section of the test. Pupils who are unfamiliar with the sound of the piano will need to experience how differing articulations, textures and dynamics will sound, and should note that contrast in some or all of these elements is built into each test.

At Grade 6 a separate question requires the candidate to identify the metre. Only commonly used time signatures are asked, as have been covered in Grades 1–5. In Grades 7 and 8 it is expected that an awareness of the metre will be integrated into candidates' observations about the piece.

Perception of pitch tonality and key relationship

In Grades 6 and 7 candidates are asked about cadences and modulations. The cadence question in each grade allows for the answer to be any of the four standard cadence formulae. In Grade 6 the cadence will always be that which closes the piece; in Grade 7 the cadence may be from any phrase encountered during the course of the performance. In Grade 8 it is expected that observations about any cadence or modulation encountered will be included in the analysis offered for Question 1, although the variety of pieces encountered at this grade, including modal, atonal and bitonal, is such that comments on cadences and modulation will not always be appropriate.

The modulation question builds on the perception of tonality explored from Grade 2. In Grade 6 all the pieces are in major keys and contain a modulation in the original version, heard several times in an identical form. The modulations are confined to one key sharper (dominant) or flatter (subdominant), or to the opposite mode (relative minor). In Grade 7 all the pieces are in the minor, and the modulation forms part of a changed ending. For this reason the modulation question finishes the set of tests for the grade, and is heard only once to ensure that candidates do not answer the question simply by referring the closing key to the known key that would start any repeat playing. Here the options move slightly farther afield, with one minor option (the subdominant) and two majors – the relative major and its dominant. Note that as the dominant in a minor key is itself minor, the dominant of the relative major can also be thought of as the relative major of the dominant. Teachers and candidates should make their own decision as to which approach they prefer to take. (They may instead prefer to think of the new key as the major key based on the flattened leading note of the original scale.)

Perception of change

At Grades 6–8 candidates will be asked questions relating to changes made by the examiner to the test piece, which by this stage in the test will have been heard a number of times. In each case candidates are shown a copy of the test piece and asked to locate and explain changes made to it in subsequent playings. This question develops reading skills and ear-to-eye links, as well as musical memory (of pitch, rhythm and other elements) over an increasing timescale and in a widening variety of musical contexts, as well as the ability to recognise characteristics in a piece of music and make judgements about them. The demands of this question increase in a carefully structured way, beginning in Grade 6 with two changes to the melody line, which may be to the pitch, the rhythm or the articulation. In Grade 7 there are three changes to find to pitch and rhythm. The pitch changes will be confined to the melody line, although the entire texture is now under scrutiny for changes to the rhythm. By Grade 8 it is expected that the well-prepared candidate, who may have followed the progression of the tests from Grade 1, will be suitably equipped to locate and identify the three changes to rhythm, harmony, articulation, dynamics or tempo. These changes thus cover all aspects of the piece in question, and therefore replicate closely the real-life situation of the musician applying their skills in perception and appraisal either to their own performance or as an informed listener.

Teachers and candidates should be aware that changes at these grades may cover more than one note, as when a *legato* passage is played *staccato*, a *forte* phrase is changed to *piano* or the harmony of a discrete passage or part of a passage is altered. It will be noticed, however, that care has been taken to make sure that the alterations are both clearly differentiated from the original text and, where possible, well separated from each other. While taking this test, candidates are strongly advised to take advantage of the option to give part or all of their answer after the first playing; if they can identify one or two changes the first time through they will then be free to concentrate on identifying the final change(s) and/or refining their first response. Note that corrections may be made after the second playing to any answer given after the first.

Marking

In all examinations, the aural tests are worth 10% of the total marks available. Marks for the aural tests are awarded holistically; that is without a fixed number of marks being allotted to each question. This enables examiners to indicate not only whether answers were correct, but also to give due credit to promptness and alacrity of response. In general, all questions should be regarded as equally important in terms of marking. Full assessment criteria are published in the **Information and Regulations** booklet, available from Trinity Guildhall's Head Office.

Track listing

Grade	Test	Track no.
Grade 6	1	01
	2	02
	3	03
	4	04
	5	05
	6	06
	7	07
	8	08
	9	09
	10	10
Grade 7	1	11
	2	12
	3	13
	4	14
	5	15
	6	16
	7	17
Grade 8	1	18
	2	19
	3	20
	4	21
	5	22
	6	23
	7	24

CD produced and edited by Mark Rogers
Piano: Tim Grant-Jones
Trinity Guildhall is indebted to Yamaha-Kemble Music (UK) Ltd for making available both the piano selection room, at their headquarters in Milton Keynes, and the Yamaha CFIIIS grand piano for the recording of the CD.
Thanks also to Neil Farrar, Yamaha's piano technician, for his service and support.
Voiceovers by Prof. Ken Pickering, recorded at Clovelly Studios, Dover.

TRINITY
GUILDHALL

Aural Book 2

Answer Booklet

for Trinity Guildhall examinations
from 2007

Grades 6-8

Published by:
Trinity College London
89 Albert Embankment
London SE1 7TP UK

T +44 (0)20 7820 6100
F +44 (0)20 7820 6161
E music@trinityguildhall.co.uk
www.trinityguildhall.co.uk

Editor: Natasha Witts
Music processed by New Notations London
Printed in England by Halstan & Co. Ltd, Amersham, Bucks

Introduction

This booklet is intended to be used:

either in conjunction with the CD and the book **Aural 2** to check and mark candidate's answers
or by teachers or others delivering the sample tests at the piano.

It includes all the text and music heard on the CD. During examinations, examiners may vary the wording of the questions slightly, as appropriate to the situation.

The first test in each Grade shows how the answers are notated for all subsequent questions. No specialist knowledge is required to use this feature, making it possible for any parent or helper to assist with preparation by checking the candidate's answers.

Suggested answers are provided for the questions on musical features; these are not exhaustive or definitive but give an indication of the type of response required.

Teachers wishing to give further examples of cadences for Grades 6 and 7 are advised that they can download a set of alternative endings for a selection of the tests from www.trinityguildhall.co.uk/music

Contents

Grade 6

Question 1

I shall play a piece twice. Afterwards I would like you to comment on the significant features of the piece such as style, phrasing and dynamics, and also to tell me the time signature. You can answer after either or both playings. **[Play piece twice]**

Question 2

I shall play the last section again; tell me what cadence comes at the end.
[Play section marked with bracket (Q2)]

Question 3

I am going to play you a section of the piece which modulates. The opening key is **[state key; play key chord].** Please tell me into which key the music has modulated. **[Play section marked with bracket (Q3) or from beginning until closing bracket]**

Question 4

Here is a copy of the piece as I have been playing it so far. I am going to play twice a version that includes two changes in the melody line. These may be to the pitch, the rhythm or the articulation. I'd like you to tell me where the changes happened and what they were. **[Play changed version twice]**

Track number

01

Test 1 Questions 1–3 (key chord to be played for Question 3 only)

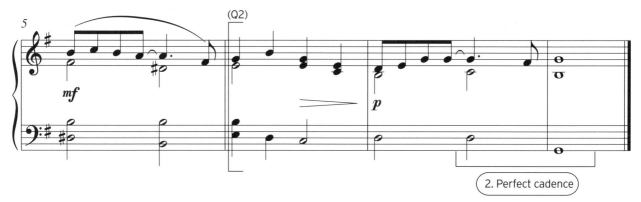

Question 1

The piece is in $\frac{4}{4}$. There are four 2-bar phrases with the first one mostly repeated at the end. Each phrase has a similar rhythm with a syncopated feature. There is a *crescendo* toward the middle, then a *diminuendo*. It finishes *piano*. The piece is played *legato* throughout.

Question 4 (changed version)

02

Test 2   Questions 1–3 (key chord to be played for Question 3 only)

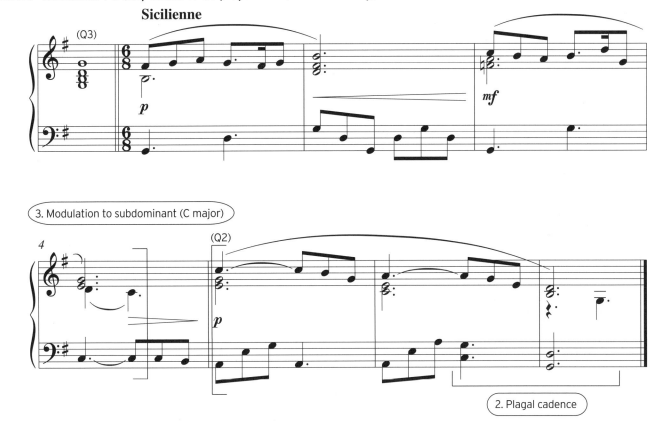

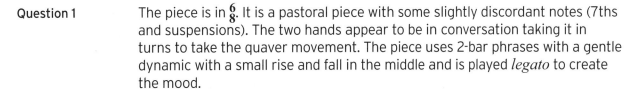

Question 1   The piece is in 6/8. It is a pastoral piece with some slightly discordant notes (7ths and suspensions). The two hands appear to be in conversation taking it in turns to take the quaver movement. The piece uses 2-bar phrases with a gentle dynamic with a small rise and fall in the middle and is played *legato* to create the mood.

Question 4 (changed version)

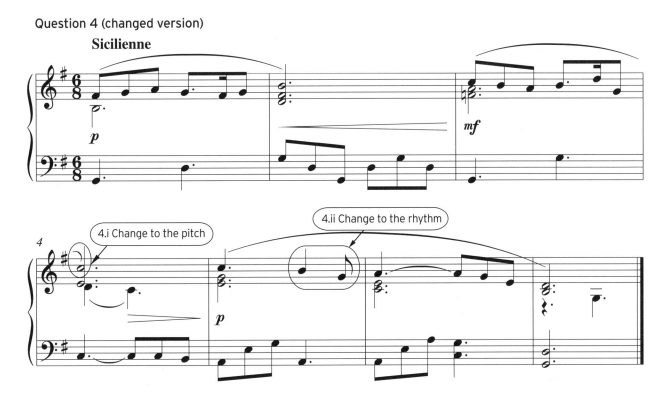

03

Test 3 Questions 1–3 (key chord to be played for Question 3 only)

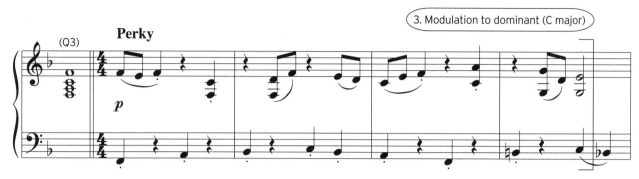

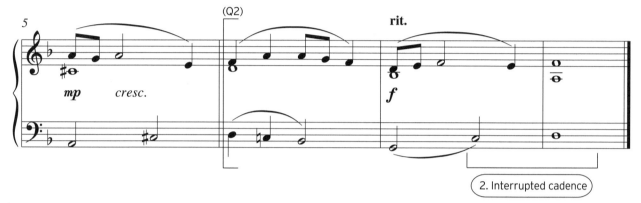

Question 1   The piece is in $\frac{4}{4}$. It is a jazzy piece; the melody notes are often played on the off-beats, while the bass notes are played on the strong beats. The bass line begins *staccato*, while the upper part has a mixture of *staccato* and *legato* notes. The second half of the piece is played *legato* and there is a *crescendo* leading to *forte* at the end.

Question 4 (changed version)

04

Test 4   Questions 1–3 (key chord to be played for Question 3 only)

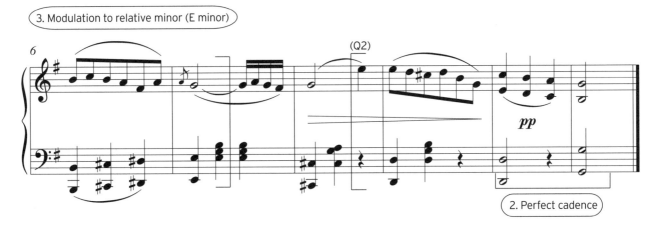

3. Modulation to relative minor (E minor)

(Q2)

2. Perfect cadence

Question 1   The piece is in ¾. It is a gentle waltz which uses grace notes (acciaccaturas) with a *crescendo* towards the middle followed by a *diminuendo* which finishes ***pp***. The phrases are generally four bars long. The piece is played *legato* throughout.

Question 4 (changed version)

4.i Change to the rhythm

4.ii Change to the pitch

05

Test 5   Questions 1–3 (key chord to be played for Question 3 only)

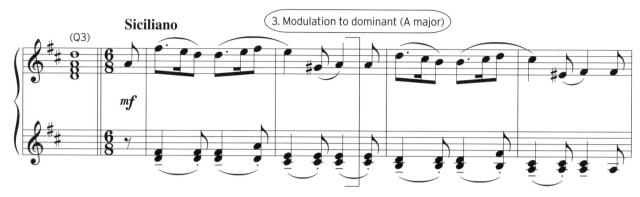

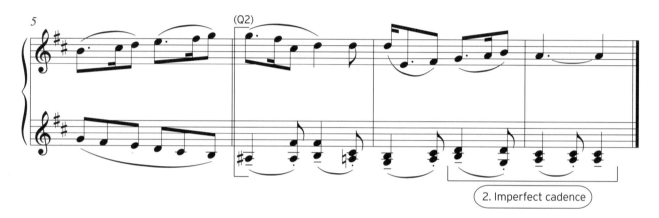

Question 1

The piece is in $\frac{6}{8}$. It is a Sicilienne-style piece using dotted rhythms to give a lilting dance feel. The first 2-bar phrase is repeated in sequence at a lower pitch. Later there is a rising scale in the melody accompanied by a descending scale in contrary motion. The piece is played at one dynamic level throughout and the melody is *legato*.

Question 4 (changed version)

06

Test 6   Questions 1–3 (key chord to be played for Question 3 only)

3. Modulation to subdominant (G major)

Question 1

The piece is in $\frac{3}{4}$. The rhythm of the opening motif is used several times, in a sequence, and is used to create mainly 2-bar phrases. The piece is mainly played *staccato*. The second half of the piece uses some syncopation. The piece begins *forte* while the second half starts *piano* with a *crescendo* at the end.

Question 4 (changed version)

07

Test 7   Questions 1–3 (key chord to be played for Question 3 only)

Question 1   The piece is in 4/4. It is a march-like piece with lots of dotted rhythms. The left hand plays a significant part often moving in step-wise motion. The second half starts quieter but builds up to *forte* for the end. Some of the right-hand dotted rhythms are *staccato*.

Question 4 (changed version)

08

Test 8   Questions 1–3 (key chord to be played for Question 3 only)

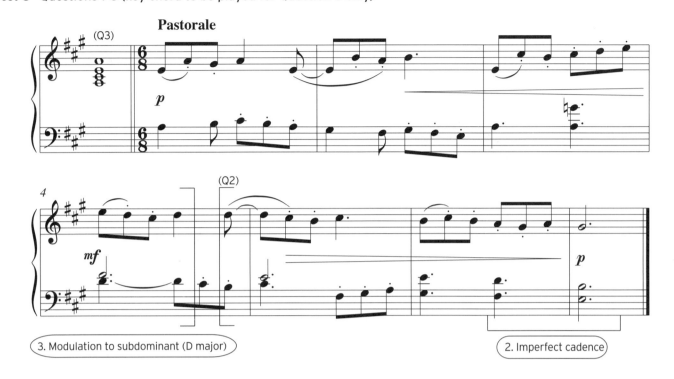

3. Modulation to subdominant (D major)

2. Imperfect cadence

Question 1

The piece is in $\frac{6}{8}$. It is a lively dance-like piece with some syncopation and a lot of *staccato* character. There is a *crescendo* and *diminuendo* in the middle. The phrasing is mainly in one-bar phrases.

Question 4 (changed version)

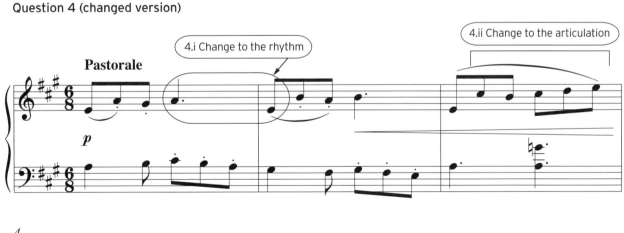

4.i Change to the rhythm

4.ii Change to the articulation

09

Test 9   Questions 1–3 (key chord to be played for Question 3 only)

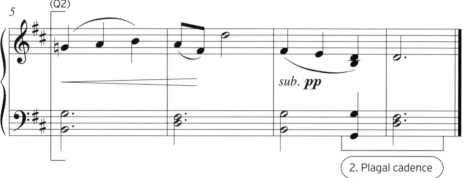

Question 1 The piece is in $\frac{3}{4}$. It is played *legato*, and mainly *piano*, and has four 2-bar phrases. The accompaniment moves in parallel (in 6ths) with the melody in the opening phrase. There is a *crescendo* in the third phrase and the piece ends *subito piano*.

Question 4 (changed version)

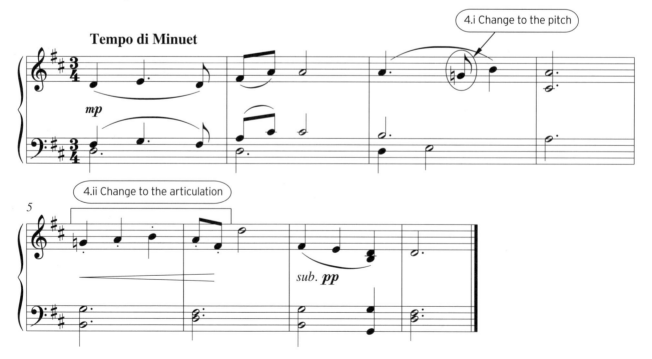

10

Test 10 Questions 1–3 (key chord to be played for Question 3 only)

Question 1

The piece is in $\frac{3}{4}$. It is in the style of a rumba or cha cha cha with accented notes on off-beats in the left-hand arpeggio figure which creates cross-rhythms with the melody. There are two acciaccaturas in the left hand giving the piece a humorous feel and the piece finishes with a 'cha cha cha' played *pianissimo*. The piece uses a mixture of *staccato* and *legato* articulation.

Question 4 (changed version)

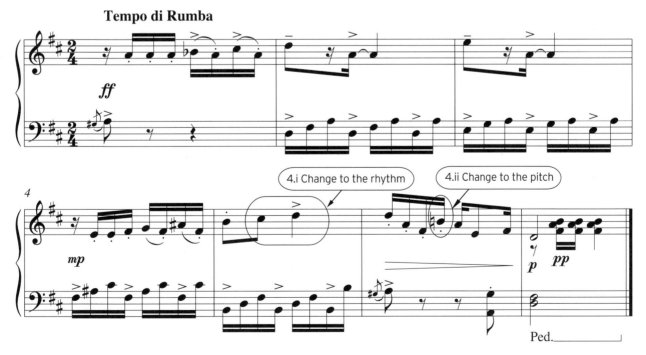

Grade 7

Question 1
I shall play twice a piece in a minor key. Afterwards I would like you to comment on the significant features of the piece such as style, phrasing and dynamics. You can answer after either or both playings.
[Play piece twice]

Question 2
Here is a section of the piece; tell me what cadence comes at the end. [Play section marked with bracket]

Question 3
Here is a copy of the first part of the piece as I have been playing it so far. I am going to play twice a version that includes three changes, which may be to the pitch (of the melody line only) or the rhythm. I'd like you to tell me where the changes happened and what they were. You can answer after either or both playings. [Play the changed version twice]

Question 4
I am now going to play the piece again with a different ending, which modulates to a new key. Tell me into which key the music has modulated. The opening key is: [State key; play key chord]. And here is the piece: [Play version of piece for Question 4]

---

*Track
number*

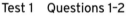
11

Test 1   Questions 1–2

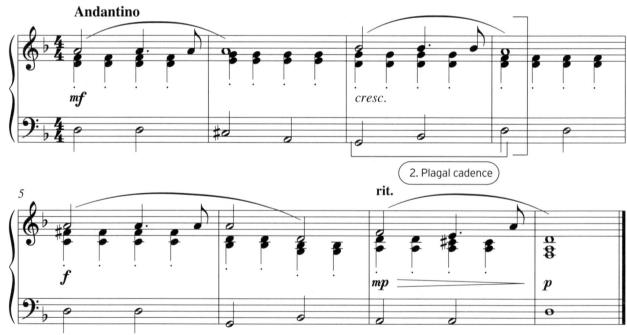

Question 1   This piece has a slow *legato* tune which is played over *staccato* chords. It has four 2-bar phrases with a *crescendo* and *diminuendo*. It finishes softly with a *rit.* The piece is diatonic.

12

Question 3

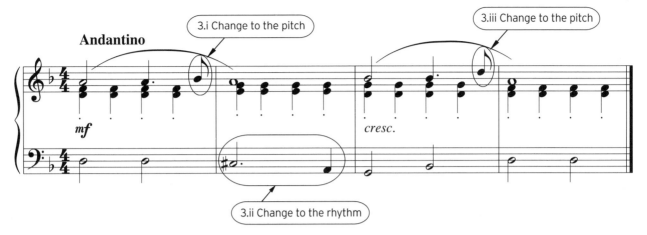

Question 4

4. Modulation to dominant of the relative major (C major)

12

Test 2   Questions 1–2

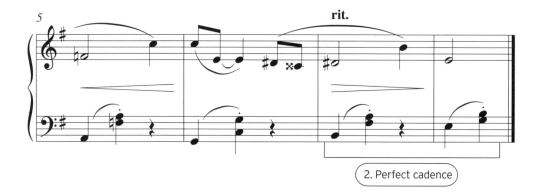

2. Perfect cadence

Question 1   This piece has four 2-bar phrases each beginning with a two-quaver anacrusis. There is a waltz-style melody which is *legato* throughout. The melody uses some wide intervals as well as movement in tones and semitones. Except for a swell in the second half the piece is at the same dynamic level throughout.

Question 3

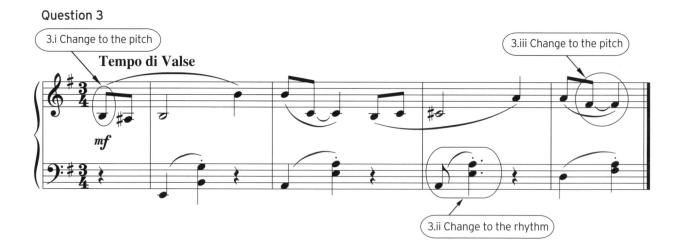

3.i Change to the pitch

3.iii Change to the pitch

3.ii Change to the rhythm

Question 4

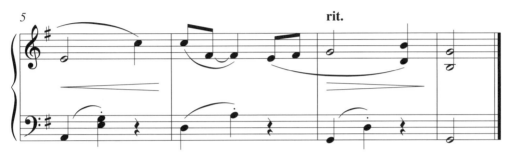

4. Modulation to relative major (G major)

13

Test 3   Questions 1–2

2. Imperfect cadence

Question 1   This piece uses mainly 2-part writing. It is in compound time in the style of a gigue. It has two 4-bar phrases. It starts *forte* and has a *diminuendo* in the second half. The melody that begins each half has a broken chord shape followed by a scale – upwards in the first half and downwards at the end. The piece is played *legato* throughout.

Question 3

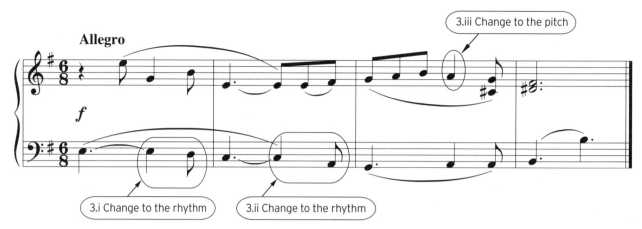

Question 4

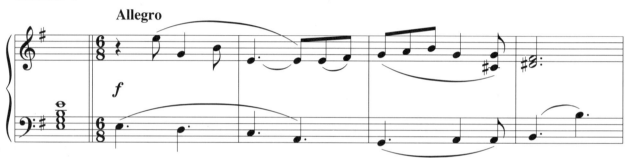

Test 4   Questions 1–2

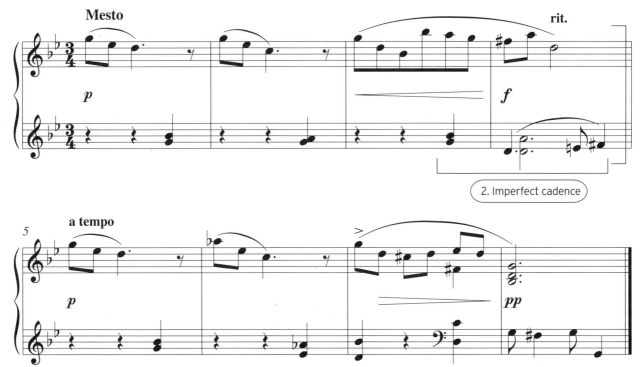

2. Imperfect cadence

Question 1   Each half of this piece begins with melodic fragments with occasional accompanying chords played in the treble part of the piano. These are followed by a 2-bar phrase that ends with a cadence. The first half ends with a *crescendo* and a *rit*. The second half ends with a *diminuendo* and without a *rit*. The piece is played *legato* throughout.

Question 3

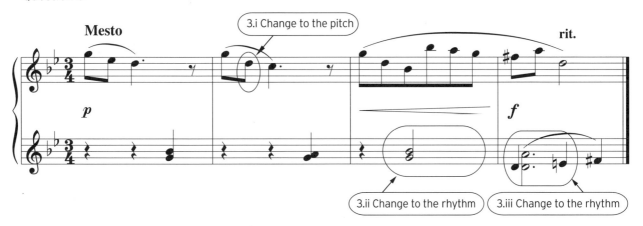

3.i Change to the pitch

3.ii Change to the rhythm   3.iii Change to the rhythm

Question 4

4. Modulation to relative major (B♭ major)

15

Test 5   Questions 1-2

2. Interrupted cadence

Question 1   This piece is like a tango with the syncopated melody line moving in 3rds accompanied by a tonic and dominant 'oom-cha' bass line. The piece has four 2-bar phrases and is mainly played *legato* in the melody and *staccato* in the bass. There is a steady *crescendo* from the beginning of the second half to the final phrase which is *forte*.

Question 3

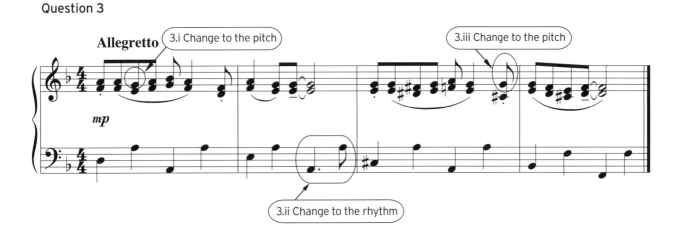

Question 4

16

Test 6   Questions 1–2

2. Plagal cadence

Question 1   This is a rock-style piece, starting *forte*, with repeated pedal note quavers in the bass. The right hand is *staccato* and begins in 3rds. The pattern changes in the middle where there is a sequence, and at the end where the same musical idea is played three times, each time quieter.

Question 3

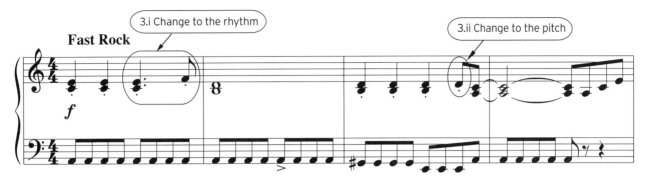

Question 4

17

Test 7   Questions 1-2

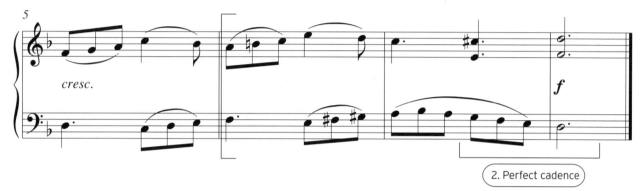

2. Perfect cadence

Question 1

This piece is in compound time, using 2-part writing with the bass line imitating the treble. It is in the style of a Baroque dance with some sequential passages and is mainly diatonic. It is mainly *legato* and uses two 4-bar phrases.

Question 3

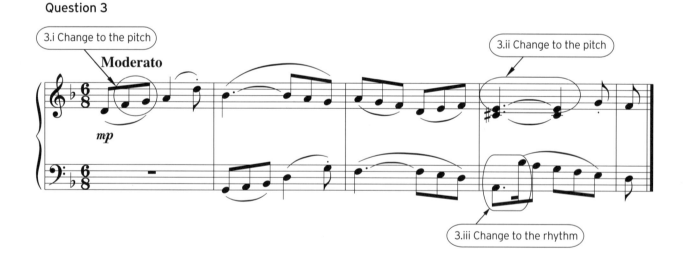

3.i Change to the pitch

3.ii Change to the pitch

3.iii Change to the rhythm

Question 4

4. Modulation to dominant of the relative major (C major)

Grade 8

Question 1

I shall play a short piece twice. Afterwards I would like you to comment on the significant features of the piece. You can answer after either or both playings. **[Play piece twice]**

Question 2

Here is a copy of the piece as I have been playing it so far. I am going to play it once as it is printed and then twice in a version that includes three changes, which may be to the rhythm, the melody, the harmony, the articulation, the dynamics or the tempo. I'd like you to tell me where the changes happened and what they were. You can answer after either or both playings.

[Play piece once, followed by the changed version twice]

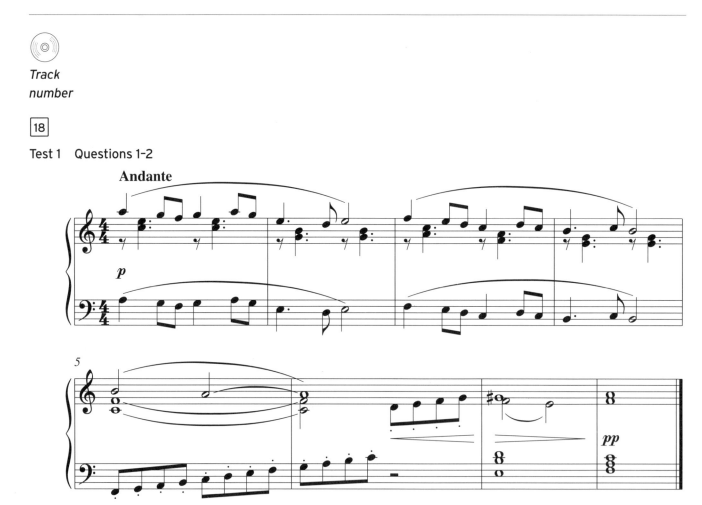

Track number

18

Test 1   Questions 1–2

Question 1	This piece begins with a *legato* melody in octaves in the high and low registers, with off-beat accompanying chords in the middle register. The piece uses the natural minor, or Aeolian mode. The final interrupted cadence uses a dominant 7th chord. The melody moves in steps, with a long, *staccato*, ascending scale (over two octaves). The piece remains within a *piano* dynamic throughout. The use of parallel voices for the melody suggests a late Romantic or Impressionistic style.

Question 2

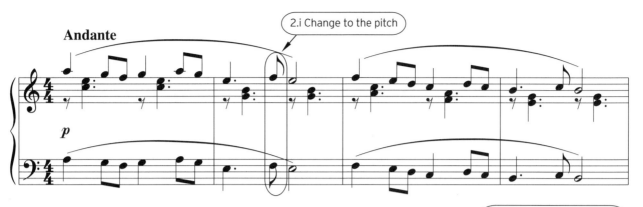

2.i Change to the pitch

Andante

p

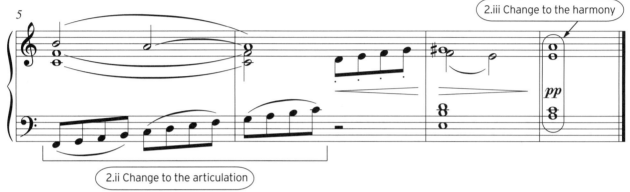

2.iii Change to the harmony

pp

2.ii Change to the articulation

19

Test 2   Questions 1–2

Vivace

ff

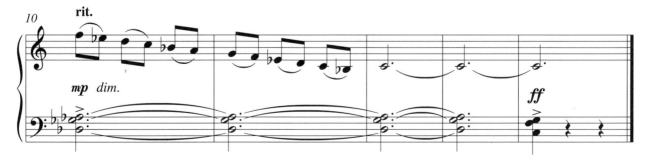

rit.

mp dim.

ff

Question 1

This is a lively, rhythmic piece with a lot of use of the interval of a 4th. The piece uses accented block chords on the first beat of each bar in the left hand and a punchy and fragmented right-hand part plays triplets and quavers. The melody becomes more *legato* with slower-moving notes, an octave drop and a hemiola. To finish there is a descending major scale in the right hand, slurred in pairs, with a *diminuendo*, coming to rest on a long discordant note. The piece ends with a surprise accented chord.

Question 2

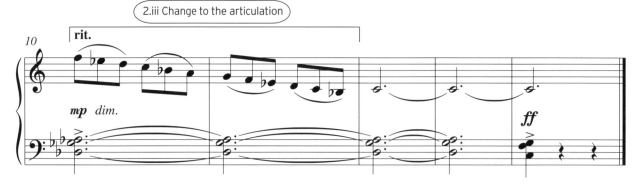

20

Test 3   Questions 1-2

Question 1   This piece has a metrical folk-like melody that is played in the bass for the second half. It is mainly in the major, but finishes on a minor chord, giving it a modal feel. The accompaniment, whichever hand it is in, is slow moving and uses mainly 2-part chords, often in bare 5ths. The piece is played quite loudly throughout, with the second phrase played *forte*. The piece uses chords I, IV and V with no chromatic notes in the chords or melody.

Question 2

21

Test 4   Questions 1-2

Question 1   A canonic, bitonal piece using two far-apart minor keys. The piece is in 3-time with the left hand entering a bar after the right. There is a climax, dynamically, in the middle and a *rit.* at the end. There are leaps as well as steps in the lines and the intervals are irregular.

Question 2

22

Test 5   Questions 1–2

Cakewalk

Question 1

This piece has a syncopated style like a ragtime or a cakewalk. The piece opens with a pedal note in open 5ths on the beat in the left hand, and jagged off-beat cluster chords in the right hand, all *staccato* and *forte*. The second phrase uses a right-hand melodic idea based on the whole-tone scale and the left hand has off-beat clusters punctuating the melody. There is a chromatic ascending passage in the right hand towards the end where there is a *crescendo* to *ff* octaves to finish. The piece has irregular phrasing.

Question 2

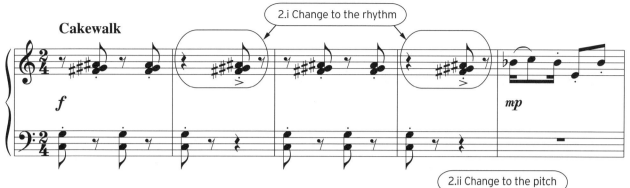

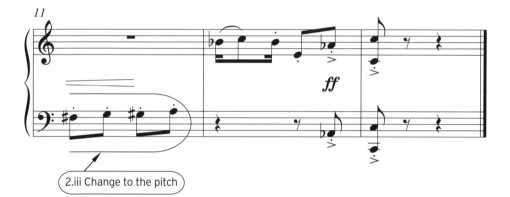

Test 6   Questions 1–2

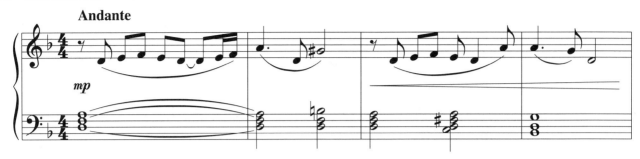

Question 1

This piece begins in a minor key and ends in its relative major. It uses a single-line melody in the right hand over block chords in the left. The harmony makes use of 7th and diminished chords. There is some gentle syncopation. The piece is in 4-time and uses 2-bar phrases. There is a *crescendo* to the middle, and the piece ends with a *diminuendo* and a *rit.* The expressive, vocal and rhapsodic melody gives the piece a late-19th-century feel.

Question 2

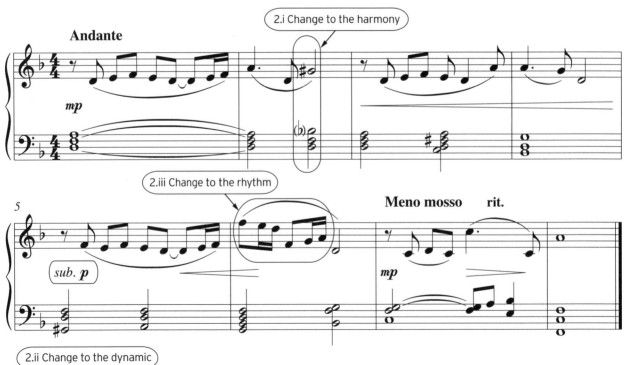

24

Test 7   Questions 1–2

Question 1   This piece is an energetic dance in 2-time, possibly a polka or a march. The melody is characterised by two *staccato* quavers then two slurred ones. There are four 4-bar phrases. The structure is an informal AABA structure, with the third phrase based on the third bar of the first two phrases. The piece is mostly in two parts with a mainly *staccato* bass line and occasional added harmony notes. Except for the third phrase, each 4-bar phrase starts *forte* and ends *piano*.

Question 2

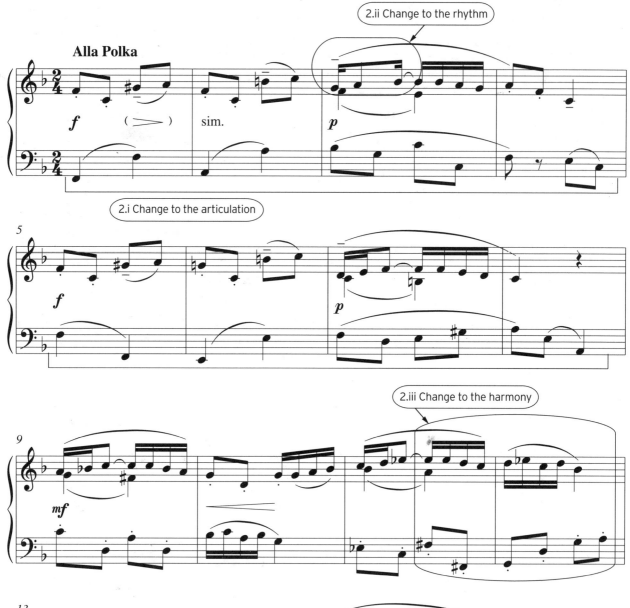

Stone Age Tales
The Great
Storm

BLOOMSBURY EDUCATION
Bloomsbury Publishing Plc
50 Bedford Square, London, WC1B 3DP, UK

BLOOMSBURY, BLOOMSBURY EDUCATION and
the Diana logo are trademarks of Bloomsbury Publishing Plc

First published in Great Britain in 2018 by Bloomsbury Publishing Plc

ISBN: PB: 978 1 4729 5026 0; ePub: 978 1 4729 5028 4; ePDF: 978 1 4729 5027 7

2 4 6 8 10 9 7 5 3 1

Text design by Amy Cooper Design

Printed and bound in the UK by CPI Group (UK) Ltd, Croydon CR0 4YY

MIX
Paper from
responsible sources
FSC® C020471